# A New Shape

For when parents
decide to separate

# A New Shape

## Anna Payne

**CWR**

Amy sniffed. She liked the smells in Theo's workshop. Today she could smell wood and paint. Theo was carving a puppet for the children. He started to smooth away the rough edges with some sandpaper.

'Theo.'

The old man looked up and smiled. 'What is it, Amy?'

'I know you're good at making things, but can you mend things as well?' Amy asked.

'It all depends on what's broken,' Theo explained. 'I love mending things, but sometimes I can't make them look the same again. My type of mending comes in different shapes and sizes.' Theo's eyes twinkled. 'Why? Do you want me to try to mend something?'

Amy nodded. She held out her special teddy and pointed to its face. 'Bertie's eye has come out and his tummy is very poorly.' She snuggled her face into Bertie's fur. 'I love him and I want him to be absolutely better, please.'

Theo reached out and took the sad little teddy. 'Bertie,' he said, propping him onto the workbench, 'you sit there while I get my sewing kit.'

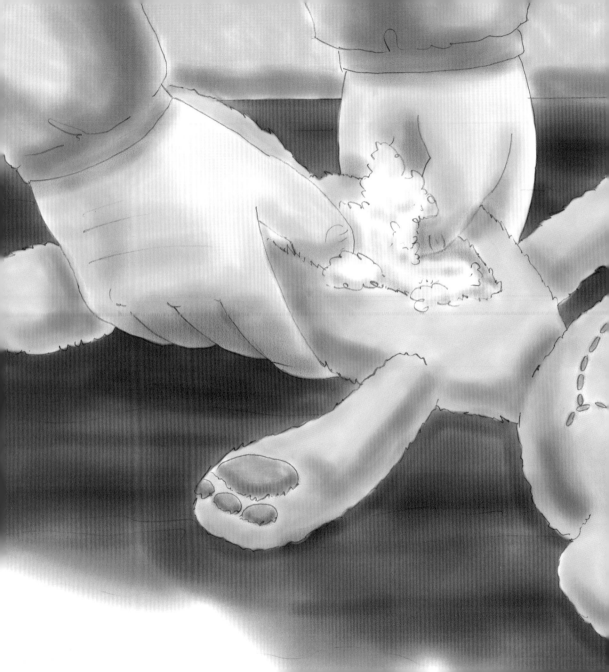

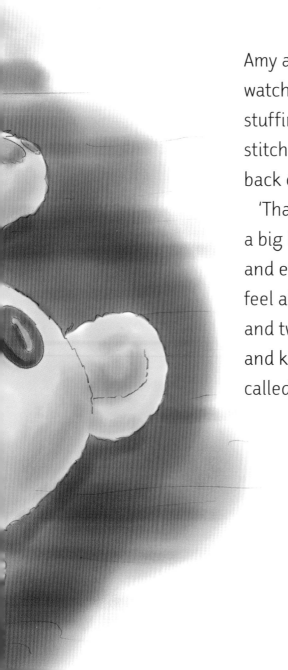

Amy and her little brother John watched as Theo gently pushed the stuffing back into Bertie and began to stitch him up. And with his eye sewn back on, Bertie looked happy again.

'Thank you, Theo.' Amy gave her friend a big hug. 'I cuddle Bertie every day and every night because he makes me feel all right again, even when I'm sad and twisty inside.' Amy picked up Bertie and kissed him. 'Come on, John,' she called, 'let's show him to Mummy.'

Theo watched the two children
walk through his gate into their
own garden, next door. He was sad
because they were feeling worried,
and he knew the reason why.

Amy and John's mummy and daddy were good friends of Theo. He had gone to their wedding years ago, and they were very precious to him, but now he knew that they were finding it hard to love each other. They were talking about what to do next and often visited Theo, asking him for his advice. Theo knew that Amy and John's mummy and daddy loved them very much. He knew they would always love Amy and John and nothing could ever change that. Theo wanted to help Amy and John understand that too.

During the night there was a huge thunderstorm. Lightning burst into the darkness and rain hammered the ground.

In the morning, Amy and John stared out of their bedroom window. They were shocked. Their garden looked as if a giant had sat down on it. Suddenly John gasped. 'Look at Theo's garden!'

At the bottom of Theo's garden was a beautiful, old apple tree. Amy and John loved to climb in its branches and pick the apples. But this morning it looked very different. The trunk had split in two. John pointed. 'Theo's crying,' he whispered.

Amy and John pulled on their wellies and raced outside to their friend.

'What's happened, Theo?' Amy held the old man's hand.

He looked down at her. 'The lightning struck my apple tree. It has split in half and lots of the branches have blown off. '

John tugged at Theo's sleeve. 'Theo,' he whispered. Theo knelt down next to him. 'Sometimes I feel like that tree, on my inside.' He tightened his little fingers around Theo's hand. 'But when I come and talk to you, it feels like you are mending me.'

Amy nodded. She knew what John meant. 'I feel like that too. When Mummy and Daddy are upset with each other, it feels like there's a storm inside my head, but when I talk to you I feel better.'

Theo put his arms around both children. 'It's all right to feel sad,' he said. 'I cried when I saw my tree this morning because it looked completely broken. First of all I wished I could mend it just like I mended your teddy. But do you remember I said I mend different things in different ways?'

John and Amy nodded.

'Look at what I'm going to do.' Theo bent down and picked up some wooden poles. As he did so, he talked to the children. 'I'm going to put these poles underneath the branches of the tree so that they can learn to hold themselves up on their own. My tree will always be a different shape but it won't be long before you will be able to climb all over it again.'

He began to hammer the first pole into the ground. 'If you're feeling confused inside your head about what's happening at home, it's best to say the words out loud. You know that you can always come and talk to me, and I will always want to listen. The other people who love you very much also want to help you understand what's happening in your family. It's just like my branches – they need some help to learn their new shape, don't they? You see, I will always help my tree to mend in the best way it can.'

Amy and John looked at the apple tree. It was sad that the lightning had split it down the middle, but Theo was right. He had different ways of mending things. Theo's poles were going to help the tree grow into a new shape. The children were sure he knew the best way of looking after things.

Theo smiled at Amy and John and held their little hands in his old wrinkled ones. 'You know Mummy and Daddy often come and talk to me, don't you?'

The children nodded.

'Well, you can come and talk to me too, at any time. Mummy and Daddy tell me they love you so much and nothing will ever change that. It is important to talk to them about how you are feeling.'

Amy patted the old tree. She felt a lot smoother and calmer inside now that they had chatted to Theo. 'And we can talk to them about what *our* new shape will be.' John smiled at his sister.

'Exactly,' Theo agreed. 'I'm sure they would both like that very much.'

As the two children left to go home, Theo smiled and waved. Amy and John waved back. They were happier now because they knew Theo would keep helping them and their mummy and daddy to discover what their own new shape would be ...

# Guidelines for Parents and Families

Communicating well with your children at this difficult time is vital. Not only will it help to prevent problems both now and later on, it will also be a long-term investment into your children's emotional wellbeing.

Remember:
- You and your children will be experiencing a range of different emotions at different times.
- You will take a while to grow accustomed to what the future holds for your family.
- Don't try to go through this alone - ask for support from family, friends or a nearby support group.
- Make time to look after yourself, as well as your family.
- Remember that all children are different and will react in their own individual ways. Coming to terms with change takes time!
- What you can manage to do, your children will learn to manage also.

## How to tell them
Try to prepare for this in advance. Think about the tough questions they are going to ask and try to deal with your own anxieties before talking to your children. As you talk to them remember that physical closeness and comfort can be very reassuring to a child when they are upset or distressed.

- Tell and demonstrate to them in different ways that you love them: both parents letting them know this simple truth is very reassuring. They will need to know that nothing that has gone on between you and your former partner will ever alter the love you both have for them. Remember that different children will understand and respond to love in different ways - don't limit yourself to just using words. Affection and physical touch, spending quality time, occasional special treats, cards or small personal gifts - all can be used to communicate love to your children.

- Tell the truth: your children deserve to know the reason why you and your former partner have chosen to separate or divorce. However, detailed reasons can be confusing for young children, so something simple like 'We can't get along together any more' is often enough. Be aware that as your children grow in age and maturity they will be able to understand more of the detail, but avoid the temptation to 'rewrite history' over time. Respond to their questions as honestly as you can, in a way that is appropriate to their age and emotional development.

- Tell them about the 'new shape' of their life in the future: acknowledge that some things will change, but that you and your former partner will ensure that they are still always cared for and that their needs are a priority.

- Give them space to reflect on what you have said and to come back to you with any questions they may have.

## Let them love you both

- Give your children permission to love both parents. Help them to know that they do not have to take sides with either of you.

- Avoid saying negative things about your former partner in front of your children. Whilst this can be very hard, it will help them to maintain a healthy relationship with each of you. It is better to remain silent than to say things about your former partner which are untrue, or you may later regret saying.

- Talk to your former partner about issues like finance and visiting rights rather than using your children as go-betweens.

- Try, as far as you are able in your discussions, to show grace and self-control rather than defensiveness.

## Help your children to express their feelings

- It is important that children know that they are allowed to talk to you both about how they feel.

- Help them to be honest. They may be reluctant to talk to you for fear of hurting your feelings. Allow them to know that you will love them whatever they say.

- Permit grief. Your children will feel upset about the loss of the life they have grown used to. Many children suffer from anxiety or depression and this can reveal itself in disruptive behaviour and anger. At times it can be hard for them to express themselves, so it may be good to encourage them to find another outlet for their emotions, like drawing, painting or journalling/writing a diary.

- Give your children time and space for these emotions to be expressed.

## Provide stability and structure

- Structure and routine will help your children feel secure even with the new shape of their lives ahead.  With very young children, keeping to the same bedtime routine, no matter whose house they are in, can help them to feel settled.

- Try to remain consistent on matters of discipline, boundaries and family expectations.

## Find support for yourself

- Look to your family and friends for the support and encouragement you need at this time. Never give in to the temptation of talking through your negative emotions with your children. Vent your frustrations on a friend!

- Look after yourself: don't be afraid to ask friends and family for help with babysitting so that you can give yourself a break and go out.

- Find out if there are any specific support groups in your local area where you can talk to others who are in the same situation as yourself.

# National Distributors

**UK: (and countries not listed below)**
CWR, Waverley Abbey House, Waverley Lane, Farnham, Surrey GU9 8EP.
Tel: (01252) 784700 Outside UK (44) 1252 784700 Email: mail@cwr.org.uk

**AUSTRALIA:** KI Entertainment, Unit 21 317-321 Woodpark Road, Smithfield, New South Wales 2164.
Tel: 1 800 850 777  Fax: 02 9604 3699  Email: sales@kientertainment.com.au

**CANADA:** David C Cook Distribution Canada, PO Box 98, 55 Woodslee Avenue, Paris, Ontario N3L 3E5.
Tel: 1800 263 2664 Email: sandi.swanson@davidccook.ca

**GHANA:** Challenge Enterprises of Ghana, PO Box 5723, Accra.
Tel: (021) 222437/223249 Fax: (021) 226227  Email: ceg@africaonline.com.gh

**HONG KONG:** Cross Communications Ltd, 1/F, 562A Nathan Road, Kowloon.
Tel: 2780 1188 Fax: 2770 6229 Email: cross@crosshk.com

**INDIA:** Crystal Communications, 10-3-18/4/1, East Marredpalli, Secunderabad – 500026, Andhra Pradesh.
Tel/Fax: (040) 27737145  Email: crystal_edwj@rediffmail.com

**KENYA:** Keswick Books and Gifts Ltd, PO Box 10242-00400, Nairobi.
Tel: (254) 20 312639/3870125 Email: keswick@swiftkenya.com

**MALAYSIA:** Canaanland, No. 25 Jalan PJU 1A/41B, NZX Commercial Centre, Ara Jaya, 47301 Petaling Jaya, Selangor.
Tel: (03) 7885 0540/1/2 Fax: (03) 7885 0545 Email: info@canaanland.com.my

Salvation Book Centre (M) Sdn Bhd, 23 Jalan SS 2/64, 47300 Petaling Jaya, Selangor.
Tel: (03) 78766411/78766797  Fax: (03) 78757066/78756360  Email: info@salvationbookcentre.com

**NEW ZEALAND:** KI Entertainment, Unit 21 317-321 Woodpark Road, Smithfield, New South Wales 2164, Australia.
Tel: 0 800 850 777  Fax: +612 9604 3699 Email: sales@kientertainment.com.au

**NIGERIA:** FBFM, Helen Baugh House, 96 St Finbarr's College Road, Akoka, Lagos.
Tel: (01) 7747429/4700218/825775/827264 Email: fbfm_1@yahoo.com

**PHILIPPINES:** OMF Literature Inc, 776 Boni Avenue, Mandaluyong City.
Tel: (02) 531 2183 Fax: (02) 531 1960 Email: gloadlaon@omflit.com

**SINGAPORE:** Alby Commercial Enterprises Pte Ltd, 95 Kallang Avenue #04-00, AIS Industrial Building, 339420.
Tel: (65) 629 27238 Fax: (65) 629 27235 Email: marketing@alby.com.sg

**SOUTH AFRICA:** Struik Christian Books, 80 MacKenzie Street, PO Box 1144, Cape Town 8000.
Tel: (021) 462 4360  Fax: (021) 461 3612  Email: info@struikchristianmedia.co.za

**SRI LANKA:** Christombu Publications (Pvt) Ltd, Bartleet House, 65 Braybrooke Place, Colombo 2.
Tel: (9411) 2421073/2447665  Email: dhanad@bartleet.com

**USA:** David C Cook Distribution Canada, PO Box 98, 55 Woodslee Avenue, Paris, Ontario N3L 3E5, Canada.
Tel: 1800 263 2664 Email: sandi.swanson@davidccook.ca

**CWR is a Registered Charity - Number 294387**
**CWR is a Limited Company registered in England - Registration Number 1990308**